DON'T BOTHER

A MISGUIDED
MINDLESSNESS JOURNAL

for people who like themselves the way they are

MILLIE O'NEILL

'Reality
continues to
ruin my life.'

BILL WATTERSON

CONTENTS

YEAH, THANKS FOR THAT

AN INGRATITUDE JOURNAL

for when you just want everyone to f**k off

'It's not your job
to be likeable.

It's your job to
be yourself.'

CHIMAMANDA NGOZI ADICHIE

'I am free of
all prejudices.

I hate everyone
equally.'

W. C. FIELDS

BEDTIME INGRATITUDE

Never go to bed without taking a moment to think about all the things that have really got under your skin that day.

Tonight I am particularly ungrateful for:

....

....

....

....

....

....

....

....

....

....

....

....

....

....

....

....

Tomorrow I expect to be even more ungrateful for:

....
....
....
....
....
....
....
....
....
....
....
....
....
....
....
....

AFFIRMATIONS

Why not adopt an affirmation or mantra to help you through challenging moments in your life?

It could be something really profound that you found on Pinterest, or just something that really **SPEAKS YOUR TRUTH**, such as:

- 'My credit rating may be bad, but my Uber rating rocks'

- 'Today I will accept the things I cannot change, and also the things that I can't really be bothered to change'

When you have thought of your affirmation, write it here:

....

....

Done?

Great. Some time has passed.

'Contentment
is knowing you
are right.

Happiness is
knowing someone
else is wrong.'

BILL BAILEY

HAD A BAD DAY?

List the ten worst things about it here:

1. _____
_____

2. _____
_____

3. _____
_____

4. _____
_____

5. _____
_____

6. _____

_____

7. _____

_____

8. _____

_____

9. _____

_____

10. _____

_____

FIND A NEW SIGN-OFF

These days, most of us find ourselves using a default email sign-off along the lines of:

- Thanks so much, Kate

- Thanks a million, Sasha

- Thanks, Noah

But isn't that just a bit galling when you have to write it at the end of an email that you're really not feeling too grateful about? Like emailing your boss to say, sure, you can work late tomorrow to fix someone else's mess. Or your university lecturer to say, yes, you absolutely understand why they won't grant you a deadline extension because your goldfish died.

You don't really want to finish those emails with 'Thanks', do you?

Use the next page to think of some new sign-off ideas that sound polite but aren't actually forcing you to say stealth 'thank you's'.

'Hell
is
other
people'

JEAN-PAUL SARTRE

MOODBOARD

Draw all of the things that put you in a really
crappy mood:

MORNING INGRATITUDE

Start your day with a healthy dose of rage.

Spend five minutes journalling about the thing
you are most dreading today:

....

....

....

....

....

....

....

....

....

....

....

....

....

....

....

....

....

Bloody Karen.

IRRITATIONS

List the ten most annoying things in your life
right now:

1. _____
_____

2. _____
_____

3. _____
_____

4. _____
_____

5. _____
_____

6. _____

_____

7. _____

_____

8. _____

_____

9. _____

_____

10. _____

_____

'Only two things are infinite: the universe and human stupidity

– and I am not
yet completely
sure about the
universe.'

ALBERT EINSTEIN

THE WORST GIFT

Mindful giving means slowing down and getting back in touch with the generous parts of ourselves. It's a thing people do.

Whether it was well-intended but misjudged, thoughtless, ugly or downright rude (nobody wants that 'Oh-God-I'm-a-wrinkled-old-hag' moment that comes with receiving fine line reducing serum as a gift from your partner's mother), take a few moments to reflect on what it was like opening that gift, and how crappy you felt afterwards.

Great. Thanks.

Tell yourself all about the worst gift
you've ever received:

....
....
....
....
....
....
....
....
....
....
....
....
....
....
....
....
....
....
....

WORDS OF WISDOM

Time has a wonderful way of showing us what really matters. And what really doesn't.

People love giving us advice, even when we haven't asked for it.

There's very little that's more infuriating than having to smile politely and listen while someone gives you their unwanted wisdom. Like when an aging Boomer tells you that all you have to do is stop buying avocado-on-toast and lattes and you'll be able to afford a house in no time, or when a friend's boyfriend mansplains to you about mortgages for said fantasy avocado-and-latte house.

List the 10 worst pieces of advice you've
ever been given:

1. _just relax_____

2. _____

3. _____

4. _____

5. _____

6. _____

7. _____

8. _____

9. _____

10. _____

THANK YOU FOR
HAVING ME

It used to be considered the polite thing to do to send your hosts a thank you card after a dinner party or visit, to express your gratitude for their hospitality.

These days, a text message or email will suffice.

But.

If you say, 'Thank you for inviting me to brunch/dinner/ movie night/your dog's christening', the person you're thanking might think you actually enjoyed yourself and invite you again.

So, yeah. Don't do that.

'The sooner
every party
breaks up,
the better.'

JANE AUSTEN

MY WORST HOLIDAY

The way people behave on social media, you'd think going on holiday is an enjoyable experience. Somehow the hour-long queues at check-in, endless delays, dodgy hotel rooms and agonising sunburn never seem to find their way on to Instagram.

Write about your worst-ever holiday on the opposite page. Remember to focus on every irritating detail, for example: the dude who fell asleep on your shoulder on the plane; the creepy Airbnb host who lives in the apartment even though the ad clearly said you'd get the whole place; the fact that museums are actually really quite boring, but you have to go otherwise you'll look uncultured.

There is nothing wrong with looking uncultured.

That holiday sucked because:

....

....

....

....

....

....

....

....

....

....

....

....

....

....

....

....

....

....

PUT IT OFF

A PROCRASTINATION PLANNER

to help distracted people avoid everything essential

'Procrastinate
now, don't
put it off.'

ELLEN DEGENERES

There is a lot of big talk out there about seizing the day, getting things done, multitasking and generally being quite annoyingly smug while you do it.

That is all fine, but what a lot of people are conveniently forgetting to acknowledge is that, if you're putting something off, it's probably because you don't want to do it.

ENTER PROCRASTINATION.

This section is all about the little things you could do instead of the big thing you're supposed to do.

PREPARING YOUR WORKSPACE

Before you can begin anything at all, you need to set up your workspace.

You can't be productive without the perfect desk, can you?

Spend some time browsing Pinterest and Instagram looking at other people's beautiful desks with rose gold pen holders, vintage anglepoise lamps and neatly arranged paper clips.

You'll probably need to head out to a few stationery shops to buy everything you need for your perfect desk.

This is also a good time to research what kind of houseplant you should have in your workspace.

Now busy yourself with reflecting on how busy you have just been:

- Give it five minutes. Perhaps you can use that time to make a coffee

- Now, check your socials and see how many likes and comments your busy desk photo has got

- Keep checking back every five minutes, just to keep an eye on things

#productivity

TERRIBLY IMPORTANT THINGS

Make a list of the three most important things
you have to do today:

1. _____

_____

2. _____

_____

3. _____

_____

Now list the three reasons why you probably
won't do them:

1. _____

_____

2. _____

_____

3. _____

_____

'I love
deadlines.

I like the
whooshing
sound they
make as they
fly by.'

DOUGLAS ADAMS

WARM-UP

Your desk is ready, your to-do list is primed, everyone knows you're a busy go-getter, and you've got a cup of coffee.

Let's not rush into things, though. Begin with a gentle mental warm-up to get your brain ready for the hours of undivided concentration ahead.

Find out how to say 'coffee' in eight languages:

1. _____

2. _____

3. _____

4. _____

5. _____

6. _____

7. _____

8. _____

What's that, you finished your coffee?

Find out how to grow coffee and whether it's possible to grow it indoors and whether it really will need watering as much as some people are bound to say it does and once you've decided not to grow your own coffee, use the space below to draw your ideal coffee cup:

'Never put off
till tomorrow
what you can
do the day after
tomorrow'

MARK TWAIN

TAKE A BREAK

Everyone knows that taking a break makes you more productive in the long run, right?

Here are some break ideas:

- Check your Insta. Any new likes or comments? **If there aren't, wait a little longer**

- Check the news. **Something might have happened!**

- Start to organise your wardrobe. Don't finish, though. **No one likes a finisher**

- Call a friend. Tell them you're too busy to talk right now. Start typing in the background so they can hear how busy you are. **You are so very busy**

- Check your Insta again. **Just in case**

SOCIAL MEDIA CLEAR-OUT

You might find you keep getting sucked into your social media feeds, indulging in a few ~~minutes~~ hours of mindless scrolling.

Think how much time you would save if you didn't have so many random people as 'friends' on Facebook, or followed a few less people Instagram and Twitter. After all, in this age of minimalism and sparking joy, why wouldn't we apply that to our online lives?

Go through your friends list and delete anyone you don't know/don't like/can't remember. That guy you went on a date with three years ago and never really called you, but occasionally throws a 'like' your way? Delete. That person you used to work with but literally have not even thought about for the last five years? Delete. That girl that was always kind of a d**k to you at school but added you to boost her numbers? Delete.

DELETE.

Very important note: At first glance, this exercise might seem to be something that will actually save you time in the long run; but fear not. You are guaranteed to fall down a rabbit hole of scrolling through the profiles and photos of people you hardly even know.

You are going to lose days to this s**t

'Procrastination
is the art of
keeping up with
yesterday.'

DON MARQUIS

DOT-TO-DOT

Complete this dot-to-dot puzzle. What could it be?

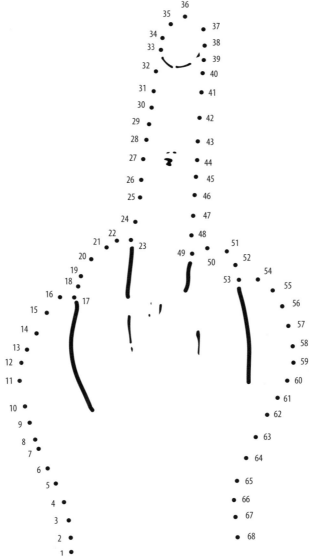

GET ORGANISED

Before you can even begin to think about the big thing you are supposed to be doing, you need to clear some headspace by doing a bunch of other little things first.

Here's a list of stuff you didn't even know you needed to do:

- Tidy your sock drawer. Spend as long as you need to hunt down all the separated pairs. Find a creative (and time-consuming) way to neatly fold and arrange your socks. Return to the drawer frequently to admire your handiwork. Definitely post a photo online

- Go through your purse and take out all the receipts and random bits of crap that have gathered there. Put the receipts in date order with every intention of going through them and checking them against your bank statement to make sure all is as it should be. (Obviously do not actually do the checking part, it is not fun at all)

- Alphabetise your spice rack. You know you want to

- Do some laundry. There's no point really getting into any work while the laundry is on. You'll only have to stop again to hang it out to dry

- If you're in the office, with no access to spice racks, sock drawers and washing machines, spend some time scheduling in a few pointless meetings. Waste some time perusing the different meeting rooms on offer. Look up the names of all the attendees on the office intranet to see what their profile photos look like

CHANGE OF SCENE

Sometimes being super productive and hard-working in the comfort of your own home just doesn't cut it.

All creative minds benefit from a change of scene (plus there is nobody at home to admire what a busy and hard-working go-getter you are).

So, every now and again (or, like, every day), head off to a trendy coffee shop and order a coffee from one of those hipster barista guys with a beard in lieu of a personality. Make sure it is a flat white (busy people don't have time for the extra inch of milk in a latte).

Set yourself up at one of the tables with your laptop. If at all possible, plug your computer in at a power socket on the other side of the room, so that everyone else who comes to the coffee shop has to navigate your power cables like some kind of millennial obstacle course and will be forced to admire the way you are getting things done.

'I wish I could,
but I don't
want to.'

PHOEBE BUFFAY

(FRIENDS)

WORD SEARCH

Word searches stretch your mind, and thus count as
a really productive activity ... don't they?

Find these words in the wordsearch opposite:

1. Busy
2. High achiever
3. Coffee
4. Bored
5. Don't do it
6. Procrastination
7. Distracted
8. Facebook
9. Instagram
10. Twitter
11. Sleepy
12. Concentration

```
G  J  U  Y  G  V  B  H  D  E  G  V  C  O  I  H  R  T  D
P  X  F  I  P  O  K  B  O  Q  U  D  C  Z  O  I  P  G  J
A  R  D  V  O  H  F  A  C  E  B  O  O  K  W  G  Y  O  F
Y  Q  O  A  J  F  B  U  V  P  K  J  D  E  T  H  Y  C  O
D  R  F  C  A  E  G  Y  R  E  C  X  S  L  M  A  G  O  P
D  I  S  T  R  A  C  T  E  D  S  I  T  B  W  C  L  N  T
O  W  W  A  D  A  N  A  N  W  E  T  T  A  P  H  N  C  M
N  T  M  I  M  C  S  T  N  T  I  G  A  B  A  I  A  E  G
D  N  M  B  W  P  O  T  T  F  C  O  F  F  E  E  T  N  R
G  B  A  F  S  W  A  I  I  G  P  F  O  K  L  V  A  T  W
E  O  I  T  M  J  S  T  N  N  F  R  D  T  L  E  A  R  O
I  R  F  M  C  F  L  L  S  M  A  H  G  M  S  R  T  A  B
I  E  M  N  D  A  E  I  T  W  U  T  F  T  T  G  A  T  L
X  D  M  H  O  N  E  U  A  S  A  R  I  N  S  T  W  I  A
R  S  W  A  N  O  P  W  G  A  S  A  T  O  B  A  I  O  B
T  O  G  T  T  O  Y  B  R  H  A  Y  W  H  N  B  W  N  B
A  I  G  H  D  O  I  A  A  O  I  Y  L  A  S  W  D  T  U
D  I  S  F  O  Y  H  T  M  F  B  N  T  A  Y  F  O  G  S
O  L  D  O  I  A  C  A  T  N  O  B  U  S  Y  G  W  A  N
S  M  M  T  T  W  I  T  T  E  R  H  T  O  I  A  V  G  W
```

THE PERFECT PEN

If you still haven't been able to get anything done, maybe it's not you – maybe it's your tools.

It's almost definitely your tools.

If you could find exactly the right pen, writing would be a lot easier.

Gather up every single pen you can find and experiment with each of them on the opposite page.

Some of them won't work even after you've tried drawing frantic zigzag lines, licked the end and then drawn more frantic zigzag lines until you've scratched holes in the pages. Some of them will leak. That's ok. Like I said:

It's definitely your tools.

WHAT WOULD YOU RATHER BE DOING?

One of the hardest things about settling down to doing a **big thing** is that we'd reaally rather be doing something else.

List ten of the things you'd rather be doing right now:

1. _eating brrra tacos_

2. _____

3. _____

4. _____

5. _____

6. _____

_____

7. _____

_____

8. _____

_____

9. _____

_____

10. _____

_____

OK, now go and do at least some of them. It would be a shame to waste such a great list.

'One thing
that's
good about
procrastination

is that you always have something planned for tomorrow.'

GLADYS BRONWYN STERN

SIGNING YOUR LIFE AWAY

Identifying what's holding you back is the key to freeing yourself from procrastination.

You know what might be holding you back?

Your signature.

Think about it: every important document you ever have to sign in your life is going to bear it. You don't want to be looking at your first ever house deed, marriage licence or Starbucks store card and seeing a signature that looks like the scrawl of a drunken two-year-old.

Use this page to try out some stylish new signatures:

....
....
....
....
....
....
....
....
....
....
....
....
....
....
....
....
....
....

'Throughout
the day I often
ask myself,
could I fall
asleep right now?

And the answer
is always a
resounding "yes".

LENA DUNHAM

Procrastinating is exhausting, isn't it?
Maybe take a nap before getting started on the **really big important thing.**

ANYWHERE BUT HERE

A MINDLESS GUIDE

for when you want to be anywhere but in the bloody moment

'Before you marry a person, you should first make them use a computer with slow internet service, to see who they really are.'

WILL FERRELL

The practice of mindfulness can bring us a sense of clarity. The problem is, we live in a world of ghosting, influencers, and Z-list celebrities with access to Twitter. Not to mention war, death, poverty, pain and suffering. Do you really want to view all of that with perfect clarity?

I think not.

Why not try softening the harshness of reality with a good dose of denial?

There. That's better.

This section is all about the beauty of escapism, wilful ignorance and distraction.

I CALL IT MINDLESSNESS.

THINGS AS THEY ARE

Mindfulness can teach us to accept things as they truly are and to escape from the cycle of dissatisfaction and unachievable desires.

So, you want to acknowledge and accept that your career is going nowhere, your bank account is overdrawn and your Tinder profile hasn't had a good match in weeks?

I didn't think so.

You know what's better than accepting things as they really are?

NETFLIX. NETFLIX AND CHEESE.

Make a list of the three shows you are
planning to watch, and what kind of snack will
best pair with each one:

1. Show: _____

Snack: _____

2. Show: _____

Snack: _____

3. Show: _____

Snack: _____

(It's totally OK if you have no idea what you are
going to watch because there is just so much to
watch. It's also OK if you just wrote 'cheese' for
each snack.)

'Wine; a constant proof that God loves us,

and loves to
see us happy.'

BENJAMIN FRANKLIN

MINDFUL BREATHING

Let's practise mindful breathing:

Sit down on a stylish-looking cushion and light an expensive candle. Set a timer on your phone for five minutes.

Close your eyes and focus your mind on your breath as you breathe **in** and **out**.

In

And **out**

And **in**

And **out**

Do you think it's been five minutes yet? Just check quickly.

4 minutes 25 seconds left on the timer?

That'll do.

Before you blow out your candle and put your cushion away, snap a photo of your meditation scene and post it online.

#mindfulness

#meditation

#zenasf**k

'If I've got
a confidence
problem,

it's that my
self-esteem is
entirely too
high.'

KATHERINE RYAN

THE BUSY MIND

Writing things down can help you become more mindful and consciously aware.

Set a timer for five minutes and sit quietly with this book open in front of you and a pen in your hand.

Concentrate on your breathing, focusing your mind on each inhale and exhale.

Every time a thought pops into your head, don't pursue it. Instead write it down on the page opposite and try to **let it go.**

....

....

....

....

....

....

....

....

....

....

....

....

....

....

....

....

....

Time's up. Now take a look at all the random s**t your brain comes up with if you leave it to its own devices for five minutes.

MINDFUL BATH TIME

There is nothing more calming and grounding than a beautiful bath.

Here's how to have a beautiful bath:

- Run a bath full of hot water and drop in some of your favourite essential oils. (Of course, nobody actually has favourite essential oils, unless your name is Rain and you live in a yurt, so just pop in some shower gel and slosh the water around a bit to mix it in)

- Light some candles so the room is lit by an ambient, flickering glow

- Take a quick photo for Instagram

#selfcare

And here's how to enjoy a bath:

- Now, pop the lights back on (if you can't find the switch in the dark, it will probably be wherever you remember last seeing it)

- Don't look in the mirror. You're two shades beyond alarmingly flushed. It's ok. The lights were off when you took the photo

- Drag a kitchen chair into the bathroom and prop your iPad up on it. You might need to trail the power cable across the floor and into the hallway. (Why aren't there ever power sockets in bathrooms? Oh yes. Safety)

- Plop yourself into the tub and enjoy a happy hour or so splashing about and watching *Parks and Rec* or the latest hot programme on Netflix

#reality

'Don't
make me an
optimist.

You will ruin
my life.'

MINDFUL EATING

**Even the most cynical among us can get
on board with the whole meditation thing if
it involves food.**

right?

So, get yourself a square of chocolate, or a small scoop
of ice cream, or some other small but delectable treat.

Close your eyes and veeeeeeeery slowly, put the food in
your mouth. Really notice how it feels on your tongue,
how it tastes. If it's chocolate or ice cream, notice the
way that it starts to melt.

I believe the idea here is that you suddenly become
super mindful and aware of the sensations of eating
and enjoy your tiny square of chocolate or single scoop
of ice cream.

But I generally find that I just get a bit bored and eat it,
then eat some more. After all, who, in the entire history
of people eating chocolate, ever stopped at just one
square?

Now that's something to think about.

Now you've had a think, make a list of the people
you've ever had anything to do with who are
actually very likely to have stopped at one square:

And are you friends with that person?
(I've made this easy to answer):

/ NO

DISCONNECT

**We could all use a break from the constant stream
of notifications, new posts and DMs.**

So just go ahead and delete your social media accounts.

Oh. That's quite extreme, isn't it?

Okay, just deactivate them.

Ah. But then everyone will wonder where you've gone
and people you don't actually like might think you've
deleted them and be offended even though you haven't
spoken for four years.

Fine, just delete the apps from your phone. You
can still access them from a computer, but you'll
have to be more mindful about it.

Ooh, though. You might miss something.
Maybe just pop your phone on airplane mode for an
hour or so?

But then someone might really need to get hold of you.

Ah ha! Put your phone on silent.

Yeah, of course it's on silent already. Whose isn't?

MINDFUL DRAWING

Here is a page for doodling. If anybody asks, you
are doing mindful drawing:

BREATHING

Yep, more breathing. Apparently, it's kind of a **big deal.**

So, let's begin:

- Take a deep breath in, and feel the air filling your lungs

- Hold it for the count of three

- Then slowly exhale

Congratulations, you have done breathing.

Just like you do all the time. But this is deliberate breathing. This is on-purpose breathing.

And that means you can smugly tell people all about it afterwards as if you are some kind of **MAGICAL OXYGEN GURU**.

'I always
wanted to
be somebody,

but now I
realise that
I should have
been more
specific.'

LILY TOMLIN

TIME TO REFLECT

So, let's say that you have practised mindfulness and achieved the state you set out for – a calmer, quieter mind.

Aaaaaaaaah.

Breathing in...

...and out

Hmmmmmm.

Are you bored yet?

Go on, you are a bit bored. I just saw you open your eyes a little. Have you watched everything on Netflix? You haven't? You need to catch up. What if someone tweets about a show you've not watched yet? Also you need to Skype your cat. And stalk your ex on Facebook. And filter the hell out of your latest Instagram shot. And think about next month's holiday. And last week's electricity bill. And how weird feet are — seriously. What are toes all about? And toenails? I mean, come on. Like little miniature talons. That's a weird word. Talons. Eagles have talons. I've never actually seen an eagle in real life. I guess they're kind of rare. Let's do a Google image search for an eagle. That one's kind of cool. Haha, look, that one's a meme. A grumpy eagle. Share that with Kate, she loves bird memes. Which makes me think, I wonder how Kate's doing? She was dating that guy, Mark somebody. He was a bit weird, but he made a bloody good White Russian. I could really go for a White Russian now, actually. I might just look up the ingredients... damn it, we're out of milk. I guess I could go and get some, but it's kind of late. How did it get so late? It's already 11pm. It was 8pm a moment ago, I'm sure of it. The whole evening just disappeared. Where did it go? OK, there was an hour or two lost on YouTube. Ever since they introduced that autoplay function it's just so hard to tear yourself away. You might miss something good. Like that one about cats that are scared of cucumbers. That was hilarious. We should try it on Lucas's cat. I might text him and ask him if he has a cucumber......

GOOD THINGS COME TO THOSE WHO ... WAIT, WHERE AM I?

The modern world is full of distractions. From our phones to our TVs to our laptops, it's not uncommon for us to be viewing three screens at a time, holding a conversation, while also checking Facebook and trying to watch a film and text simultaneously.

We are constantly over-stimulated and overstretched.

But consider this: if your mind is constantly distracted by Twitter feeds and cat videos, you'll never have a chance to reflect on your life, your feelings, the moment you are in or the generally catastrophic state of the world.

THIS IS A GOOD THING

NAH

A DEMOTIVATION
DIARY

for lazy people who really can't be a*sed

'Hard work never
killed anybody.
Still, there's
no use taking
chances.'

EDGAR BERGEN

Motivation is a real thing these days. Everyone likes sharing inspirational quotes on Pinterest (why are they always in such awful fonts?) and talking about goals and achieving things and, honestly, it's quite tiring, isn't it?

THIS IS A DEMOTIVATION DIARY.

It's an antidote to all of the above. It's really just about doing the bare minimum, not bothering too much, and being OK with that.

GOOD MORNING, SUNSHINE

It can be hard to get out of bed, but a morning routine can really help.

A green juice, a morning run, creative journalling and some light oil painting.

All before breakfast.

Say what?

Or, let's try something more realistic:

6am: Alarm sounds. Snooze

6.15am: Snooze

6.30am: Snooze

7am: Snooze just once more

7.30am: Shower time. Someone is already in there. Oh well, back to bed

8am: Snooze

8.30am: Late! Clothes on, coffee, out the door

8.50am: Miss your train

9am: Back to bed. Try again tomorrow

'I have a new philosophy:

I'm only going
to dread one
day at a time.'

CHARLES M. SCHULZ

SEEKING PERFECTION

**We've all heard the phrase 'nobody's perfect'.
And it's true. In reality, there is no such
thing as perfection.**

Which means there is very little point in trying to do anything, as it will always be, at best, just less than perfect.

Next time somebody asks you why you aren't bothering with a project, kindly explain to them that you are a perfectionist, and therefore can't partake in anything that will be less than perfect.

Which is everything.

'There's always someone cooler than you.'

BEN FOLDS

'By faithfully working eight hours a day, you may eventually get to be boss and work twelve hours a day.'

Robert Frost

BEING PART OF A TEAM

So, you've been given a group project. It doesn't matter whether you're at school, university, or 15 years into a career. Group projects are always the same.

You could work really hard on this project, but you know who's going to get the credit, don't you?

Yeah, that's right. Andy.

Andy is going to get all the credit. Because group projects are always the same, and every group project has an Andy.

SO WHY BOTHER?

P.S. Andy, if you're reading this, stop taking all the credit.
Sincerely,
Everyone who's ever been stuck in a group project with you.

'Getting fit is all about mind over matter. I don't mind, so it doesn't matter.'

ADAM HARGREAVES

WORK IT OUT

We all know exercise is good for us.

It's also hard work.

Do you know why it's hard work?

Because you hate it.

Also, the gym is far away, your workout gear is in the wash, and you haven't got the right kind of yoga mat or trainers...

TRY AGAIN NEXT WEEK.

YOU CAN DO IT

Sometimes all we need is just to believe in ourselves a little more.

Try this exercise to reinforce your sense of self-belief.

Use the page opposite to write out the words I CAN DO IT over and over again, in big, powerful letters.

....

....

....

....

....

....

....

....

....

....

....

....

....

....

....

....

....

There you go. Sense of self belief reinforced. Done. It's
not like you actually said you would do it. It's just nice to
know you can. If anything, now that you know you can do
it, there's really no need to try.

'Laziness is
nothing more
than the habit of
resting before
you get tired.'

JULES RENARD

JUST SNOOZE IT

**Why not take a nap before you're
actually sleepy?**

So efficient.

TO-DON'T LIST

Write down 10 things you really shouldn't
do today:

1. _____

_____

2. _____

_____

3. _____

_____

4. _____

_____

5. _____

_____

6. _____

_____

7. _____

_____

8. _____

_____

9. _____

_____

10. _____

_____

Now, tick them all off.
There you go: all the satisfaction of ticking things off your list, without actually having to do them.

'Kids, you
tried your best
and you failed
miserably.

The lesson is, never try.'

HOMER SIMPSON

HALF-ASS IT

Use the page opposite to write a list of ideas for things you can probably do with about half the effort you're currently putting into them, just by making a few easy changes.

For example, instead of constantly loading and unloading the dishwasher, just leave the stuff in there at the end of the next cycle. Take things out when you need them, put them back in when you're done. Just, you know, turn it on every now and again.

Or, by committing to a routine of sleeping late, dry shampoo and a variety of hats, you can stop bothering with washing your hair and save money on shampoo.

Win-win!

1. _____

2. _____

3. _____

4. _____

5. _____

6. _____

7. _____

8. _____

9. _____

10. _____

DEAR ME

Think about all those things in the past that seemed like a really **big deal** and actually turned out to be not a very big deal at all (when's the last time someone asked you what grade you got for that science test when you were fifteen?).

Write a letter to your past self, telling them not to bother with all that stress, because, honestly, what's the point?

Be sure to add the date so that **future** you can look back and see what **recently past** you told **distantly past** you, and benefit from the same advice!

Date ___/___/__

Dear_____,

_____
_____
_____
_____
_____
_____
_____
_____
_____
_____
_____
_____
_____
_____
_____
_____

Love from me x

BEDTIME DEMOTIVATION
WIND-DOWN

Today was exhausting. Make a list of five
important things you didn't bother doing:

1. _____

2. _____

3. _____

4. _____

5. _____

Guess what? The world didn't end, did it? (And actually,
if it had, would you have thought: 'Gosh, it's the
apocalypse. I'm so pleased I finally dropped off my dry-
cleaning'?)

'The world is
a stage, but
the play is
badly cast.'

OSCAR WILDE

'If you live long enough, you'll see that every victory turns into a defeat.'

SIMONE DE BEAUVOIR

Use this page to draw a picture of how well you're going to sleep tonight knowing you didn't waste any energy on S**T THAT DOESN'T MATTER.

GOAL-GETTER

**Setting goals is a really important part
of motivation.**

If you don't have any goals, you have nothing to work towards.

Think about it. Nothing to work towards. No work. Doesn't that sound good?

Yes it does.

Conclusion: DON'T SET GOALS.

If you like, you can use the rest of this page to
not-set some goals:

....
....
....
....
....
....
....
....
....
....
....
....
....
....
....
....
....

A TIME FOR REFLECTION

So sure, getting motivated, pumped up and ready to take on the world might work for some people.

But for everyone else, there's always the snooze button.

I mean, why did they even invent the snooze button if we weren't supposed to use it?

'Most harm is done by people who are awake.'

JEREMY HARDY

GIVE IT YOUR LEAST

A BAD-HABIT BULLET JOURNAL

for all the things you'll never change

'The trouble with
having an open
mind, of course, is
that people
will insist on
coming along
and trying to put
things in it.'

TERRY PRATCHETT

Ah, the bullet journal. The millennial's answer to the Filofax. It's sort of like a normal notebook but it has dots and it's a little bit more ... smug.

This section will help you get started on your very own, very smug bullet journal journey. (Because everything is a journey these days.)

Welcome to a world of lists, symbols and habit tracking. I hope you have a lot of washi tape and colourful pens. S**t's about to get real.

REAL DECORATIVE.

PRACTICE MAKES PERFECT

Bullet journals are supposed to be a great productivity tool, but the most important thing to know about them is that you can spend literally hours practising writing out the days of the week in pastel-coloured paintbrush pens, so that by the time you've finished preparing your picture-perfect bullet journal pages for the week, it's three weeks later and you haven't done anything.

But you can still post a picture of your gallery-worthy calligraphy skills on the 'gram.

Start by replicating this font:

Monday

And then make sure you have figured out how to write out the other days of the week in the same font. All of this must be perfect before you can start committing your habits to paper.

TO-DO LISTS

To-Do lists are at the very heart of mindful planning.

If writing to-do lists wasn't a mindful thing, there would be no need for bullet journals. You'd just use old envelopes, and important documents and perhaps even a note pad to jot down your to-do lists. But as writing to-do lists really is a mindful exercise, and because you need a bullet journal to realise your list of things to do, here are a few tips to get you started:

- Always include a few things you've already done. Just to kick things off with a real sense of accomplishment

- Break tasks down into easy-to-achieve chunks:
  Wake up. **Well done**
  Drink coffee. **WINNING AT THIS**
  Turn on laptop. **You are on fire**
  Write 4,000-word report that was due last week. **Ah**

- Symbols. Symbols are, hands down, the best thing about bullet journal lists. You can come up with a series of symbols to use to show what stage each item is at. And one of these symbols should allow you to move the task to another day.

I repeat: **there is a symbol that allows you to move the task to another day.**

Like, nah, not today, thanks. And instead of that making you feel a bit queasy and guilty, it's fine, because the bullet journal system lets you draw a little 'do it later' symbol and – tah-dah! Netflix time

HABIT SURVEILLANCE

Set up a tracker for all of your favourite habits.

Note I said 'favourite' habits. They don't have to be good ones.

I've included some ideas below to get you started, and there's space to add your own awesome habits.

- Playing Candy Crush on the loo

- Eating chocolate for literally no reason other than it was there

- Buying a coffee you can't really afford

- 'Accidentally' ordering a bunch of clothes

- Squeezing a zit (so very satisfying)

- Getting into your gym kit and ending up just having brunch instead

- Grating cheese for whatever you're cooking and then just eating half of it straight out of the bowl without adding it to the recipe

Habit

M T W T F S S

'Your net worth
to the world
is usually
determined by
what remains
after your

bad habits are
subtracted
from your good
ones.'

BENJAMIN FRANKLIN

NET WORTH

Use the page opposite to calculate your net worth.

Not the financial one (unless you really fancy a trip to misery town), but the one Mr. Franklin's talking about. List some of your good habits and some of your bad habits, and compare.

As it's quite a complex (and potentially depressing) thing to think about, you might prefer to use the page to try drawing a perfect circle. It's OK if you then spend hours wondering whether or not you're a psychopath because, like us, you think you read somewhere that psychopaths draw perfect circles.

'You know what
life is like?
We're all extras
in someone
else's movie.'

CHRIS D'ELIA

THE MORE ACTIVITIES, THE BETTER

Use the page opposite to create a smug weekly planner that you can take photos of and post on Instagram.

Be sure to include lots of gym visits, evening classes and fun activities.

Don't worry, you don't actually have to do any of them. It's just that the planner wouldn't look as impressive if it just had 'Stay home and watch TV in pyjamas while eating peanut butter straight from the jar' as the activity every single evening.

(By the way, **kudos**. That sounds like a great night. May I join you?)

'I don't have
any bad habits.

They might be
bad habits for
other people,
but they're all
right for me.'

EUBIE BLAKE

HAPPY BIRTHDAY

Create a beautiful list of all the important
birthdays that you're bound to forget this year:

SPENDING TRACKER

Tracking your spending for a week can give you a great insight into your money habits.

I wouldn't recommend writing down everything you spend your money on. It can be kind of depressing. Just record the stuff that sounds good. Like so:

- A selection of organic vegetables from the health food shop. **Yes**

- A lifetime subscription to a magazine promoting living in the back of a vehicle designed to transport potatoes or ladders. **Hell yes**

- A pricey latte and a cheap outfit that you're never going to wear? **Nope**
  Let's just ignore that one. If it's not in the tracker, it didn't happen.

#denial

#budgets

#gettingitdone

There's an example of a fairly standard table below, or why not spend hours designing your own on the next page?

date	item	cost

'We like lists because we don't want to die.'

UMBERTO ECO

LIQUID ASSETS

You might have seen that a lot of people like to use their bullet journals to track how much water they're drinking. Because, you know, as adult humans, we may forget to drink vital liquids unless we get to colour in a square with a blue highlighter as a reward.

If you want to get in on that s**t, may I suggest that you make things a little more interesting and track not only glasses of water, but also every single liquid you consume today? In true bullet-journal style, you can colour code it – blue for water, dark brown for coffee, orange for juice.

Do you have a gin-coloured highlighter?

GOALS

Yeah, I know. I've mentioned goals once or twice already. They are kind of a **big deal** in the journal world. And honestly, your bullet journal is a great place to list your goals.

Write down your top five aims this year.

Learn a new language? Pay off your credit cards? Get your head around what the f**k is happening in the world of politics? (Spoiler: no one knows.)

Remember to ~~waste~~ spend some time making the list look super pretty.

Done!

Note I said to list your goals. Not necessarily achieve them.

It's a great-looking list, though. **Good job!**

MOVIE LIST

If you are feeling a bit overwhelmed by how much you have to do, just take a few minutes to put together a list of all those films people are always telling you that you just have to watch.

Geez, now you have a load of movies to watch.

Sorry for adding to your to-do list.

SO WHAT HAVE WE LEARNED?

I hope you've enjoyed your bullet journal experience. Who knew that having dots instead of lines could make lists so much more satisfying?

Seriously though. As much as I have messed around here, and enjoyed chatting about procrastination, mindlessness, demotivation and smug, smug lists, there is a bit of an overarching theme to bear in mind.

I hope you remember it next time you can't be bothered to get out of bed, or you find yourself facing the unwelcome prospect of a crappy meeting at work, or if you're still feeling kind of bummed out about how *Game of Thrones* ended.

You're really, honestly, genuinely fine.

JUST AS YOU ARE.